Samuel

susanna gretz

Teddybears movi

Hippo Books
Scholastic Publications Ltd
London

Once there were five bears in bed.
Today was moving day.
Everyone was thinking about it — everyone
except Robert and Fred.
Robert was pretending it wasn't
moving day at all.
Fred, the dog, was fast asleep.

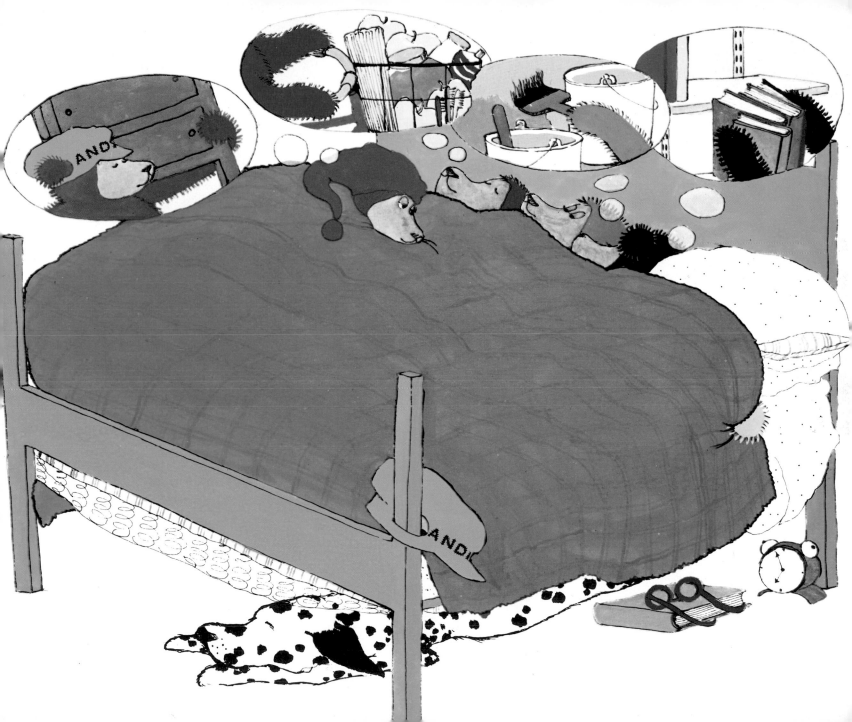

"Moving won't take long if everyone helps," said Andrew.
"And we can have spaghetti afterwards," said William.

"Robert, you should help, too,"
said Charles.
"But Robert always spills
everything," said Andrew.

"And loses everything,"
said William.

"And forgets everything,"
said John.

I DO NOT.

I DO NOT.

Meanwhile, the heaviest things
were loaded onto the van.
"Wait," cried William,
"there's some left-over milkshake
in that fridge!"

"Have *you* packed, Robert?" said Charles.
"You're in the way, Robert," said John.

Robert wanted to carry his tent.
"Look out!" said Andrew.

When everything was ready,
they all set off for the new house.
"I know the way," said Charles,
who had made a map.

Charles' map looked like this:

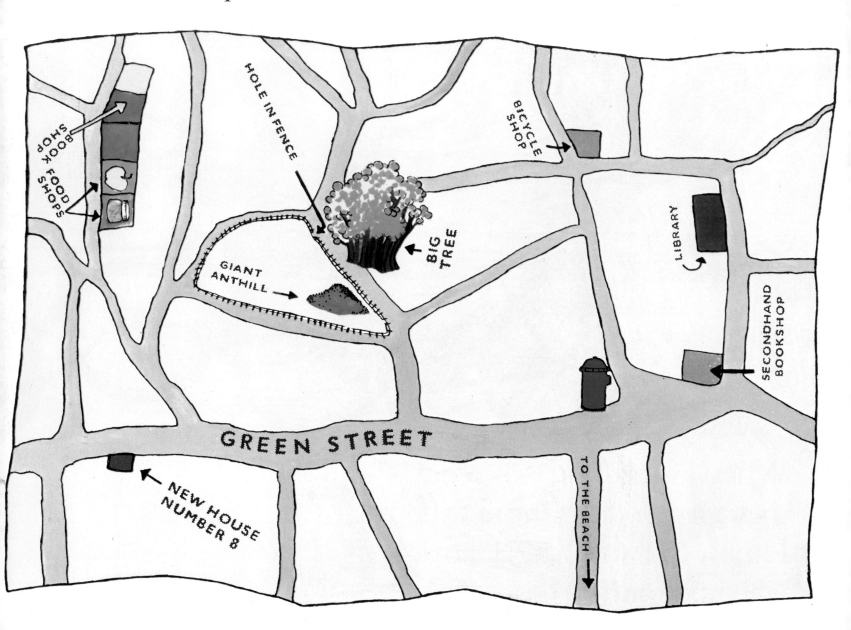

BOOK SHOP

FOOD SHOPS

HOLE IN FENCE

BICYCLE SHOP

BIG TREE

GIANT ANTHILL

LIBRARY

SECONDHAND BOOKSHOP

GREEN STREET

NEW HOUSE NUMBER 8

TO THE BEACH

Green Street was lovely . . .

. . . but Robert didn't notice it.
"Where are all my things?" he said.

Robert stopped.
He looked at the map. Which way was it?
There wasn't a bear in sight.

Lost!

Around the corner came Sara and Louise.
"Why are you crying?" they asked.
"Do you know where Green Street is?" said Robert.
"I should think so," said Sara;
"We live in Green Street."
  She and Louise showed Robert the way home.

" Where have *you* been?" said William and Andrew.
"You haven't helped at all," said John.
"Why have you been crying?" said Charles.
"Only tiny *cubs* cry," said John.
"Everyone cries sometimes," said Louise.
"They do not," said John.

Afterwards, Charles ran a hot bath.

"Let's go back to work," said Andrew.

"Doesn't the room look lovely now?" said Sara.
"Supper's ready," said Charles.

"Moving makes you hungry," said William.
Robert had another helping of spaghetti.
"It certainly does," he said.